Susie Brooks

D0654239

PAPER

PRINT

STAMP

50 fun art projects to make

9112000036437

CONTENTS

People pyramid p.48

Spongy Wrap p.26

Leafy Lions p.10

Bright bunch p.14

Swirly Snail p.30

Dangly Dragons p.22

Forky Fun p.12

LET'S MAKE ART!

Look all around you, indoors and outdoors – what can you find to make into art? How often do you throw old food packaging, scrap paper or leaflets into the recycling? Next time you do, stop and look! This book is packed with exciting ideas to help you turn ordinary things into extraordinary things.

If you want to make great pictures quickly, printing and stamping is a brilliant way to start. You can even make art using your own hands and feet! Look at the shape of them – what do they say to you? Can you see a bird, a fish, a dinosaur or an aeroplane? If not, you soon will after reading this book!

WHAT YOU NEED

You can make art with almost anything! Most everyday objects can be used to print, as long as you can wash the paint off afterwards. Search at home or in your school bag for things that have interesting shapes you can print with, paint on, cut out or draw round. In this book we'll print with leaves, bottle tops, pen lids, balloons and vegetables; and make art using coins, keys, kitchen paper, cling film, toilet rolls, lolly sticks, sponges, forks, cheese graters, freezer-bag ties and even salt and soap!

You don't need to buy lots of materials to make the projects in this book, either. Look in the recycling for old envelopes, brown paper and cardboard. Scraps of wrapping paper or magazine pages are great for decoration, as are ribbons, cupcake cases and doilies. If you like the colours on an old cereal packet or magazine photo, save it! Even black-and-white newspaper can be turned into brilliant designs.

FOR THE PROJECTS IN THIS BOOK IT ALSO HELPS TO HAVE A FEW BASIC ART SUPPLIES:

- ✓ a pencil and rubber
- ✓ scissors
- ✓ glue
- ✓ plain white paper or card
- ✓ coloured paper or card, including black
- ✓ coloured pencils
- ✓ felt-tip pens
- ✓ crayons
- ✓ a ruler
- ✓ a hole punch
- ✓ double-sided sticky tape
- ✓ a sponge
- ✓ ready-mix paints
- ✓ paintbrushes
- ✓ sponges
- ✓ coloured ink pads
- ✓ wool, ribbon or string
- ✓ bubble wrap
- ✓ kitchen paper
- ✓ newspaper
- ✓ paper plates or a paint palette

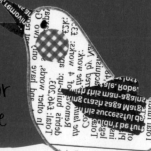

HANDY HINTS

Before you start, lay down plenty of newspaper to protect the surface you're working on.

Save scraps of paper that you have cut away — they'll be useful another time!

Work at a size you feel comfortable with — if something is too fiddly to cut, try doing it bigger.

To pick up tiny bits of paper like the circles from a hole punch, lick your finger and the paper will cling to it.

If you don't have paper in the colour you want, you can always paint your own.

When you see this **LOGO**, you might want to ask an adult to help.

There are templates on **PAGES 106–11** to help you draw some useful shapes, but do not try to copy everything exactly. Half the fun is testing ideas of your own!

Nail scissors are handy for cutting small paper shapes. Some craft scissors have a special zig–zag blade for fancy edges.

Keep a bowl of water, a cloth and an old towel nearby to clean the objects you have been printing with. Kitchen paper is useful for wiping.

IT CAN TAKE A FEW GOES TO MAKE A PERFECT PRINT. TRY THESE TIPS:

- Cover the object evenly with paint — a sponge is useful for doing this
- Press the object firmly down on the paper and **KEEP IT STILL** to avoid smudging
- Lift the object straight up again afterwards, holding down the paper with your other hand.

BATTY SILHOUETTES

Use coloured tissue paper packaging to make these batty backgrounds.

1 Tear up scraps of tissue paper and glue them to a sheet of white paper or card. Keep going until the paper is covered. Don't worry if you only have one or two colours. You can overlap the pieces to create different shades.

3 When your paper is full, draw around a mug, glass or roll of sticky tape and cut out several circles.

2 Now practise drawing bat shapes like this one. Make them small enough to fit inside your tissue paper circles. Copy them on to black paper and cut them out. There are some templates on p.30 to help you.

4 Glue a bat to each circle, then arrange them on a sheet of black paper or card and stick them down.

Make a black cat or an owl to go with your bats!

HANDPRINT ZOO

You can make a whole zoo of beautiful paper animals out of your handprints!

ELEPHANT

1 Make a handprint with your fingers and thumb spread out. The thumb makes the elephant's trunk.

You can paint some lines to make wrinkles on the trunk if you like.

2 Paint on ears, a tail, an eye, a mouth and a pink cheek.

HIPPO

1 Print with your fingers and thumb spread out. Turn the end of the thumb into the hippo's head. Paint on eyes, nostrils, cheeks and a tail.

You could add some water and reeds!

8

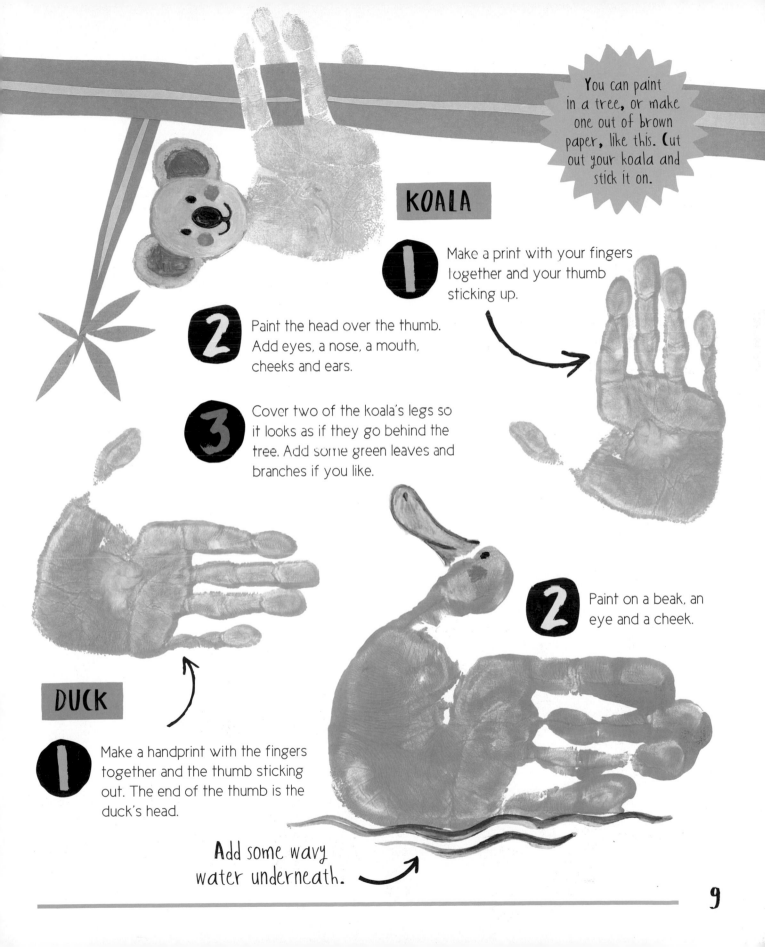

You can paint in a tree, or make one out of brown paper, like this. Cut out your koala and stick it on.

KOALA

1 Make a print with your fingers together and your thumb sticking up.

2 Paint the head over the thumb. Add eyes, a nose, a mouth, cheeks and ears.

3 Cover two of the koala's legs so it looks as if they go behind the tree. Add some green leaves and branches if you like.

2 Paint on a beak, an eye and a cheek.

DUCK

1 Make a handprint with the fingers together and the thumb sticking out. The end of the thumb is the duck's head.

Add some wavy water underneath.

LEAFY LIONS

A leaf-printed mane is perfect for the king of the jungle!

1 You can use any medium-to-large leaf for this. Cover the veiny side with orange paint and press it on to yellow paper. Add more paint and repeat. You'll need about nine leaf prints.

ears

head

THERE ARE TEMPLATES ON P.110 IF YOU NEED THEM!

tail

body

2 When the prints are dry, cut them out. Arrange them in a flower shape like the one above.

3 Cut out the lion's head, body, ears and tail from another piece of yellow paper. The head should fit in the middle of your leaves, with room around the edge.

Why not make a multi-coloured mane?

Glue on the ears, then paint the middle of them pink.

Paint on a face.

4 Glue the lion's body to the bottom of a large sheet of paper. Stick the leaves on top, then stick the head in the middle of the leaves.

Glue on the tail. You could stick another leaf print to the end of it!

FORKY FUN

Print these with an everyday fork — but remember to wash the paint off afterwards!

 Spread some paint on to a paper plate and dip in the back of a fork. Practise making prong prints, like below, on to white paper.

one fork

three fork prints in a row

2 To make a cat, print a round head like this. For the body, make several rows of prints underneath each other.

Add some whiskers.

Lots of fork prints in a circle — turn the paper as you go

Paint on some ears and a tail using a paintbrush.

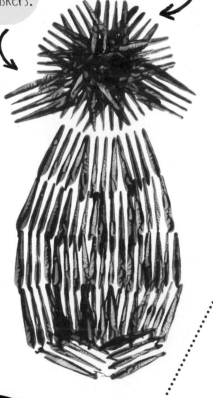

When the paint is dry, draw on a face.

3 While the paint is still wet, scrunch up a piece of kitchen paper and use it to blot the paint in the middle of the head. Add some stripes to the body, too.

What other animals can you print?

TRY A WHITE SHEEP!

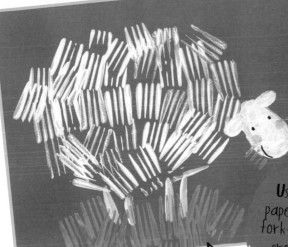

Use coloured paper. Why not fork-print some green grass.

OR A HEDGEHOG!

Or a forkupine! Print the forky prickles first, then paint on a head.

OR SOME FORK FLOWERS!

Press the fork down and rock it backwards to print the part below the prongs. Then paint on a stalk and leaves, and you have a flower!

13

BRIGHT BUNCH

Transform old scraps of wrapping paper, wallpaper and other patterned paper into a colourful vase of flowers.

1 Cut out rough circular shapes from different coloured papers and stick smaller ones on top of the larger ones.

Here are a few ways to make your flowers:

 2 Cut out petal shapes and arrange them in a flower design, like this.

3 Overlap some large round shapes in a circle, then stick a smaller one in the middle.

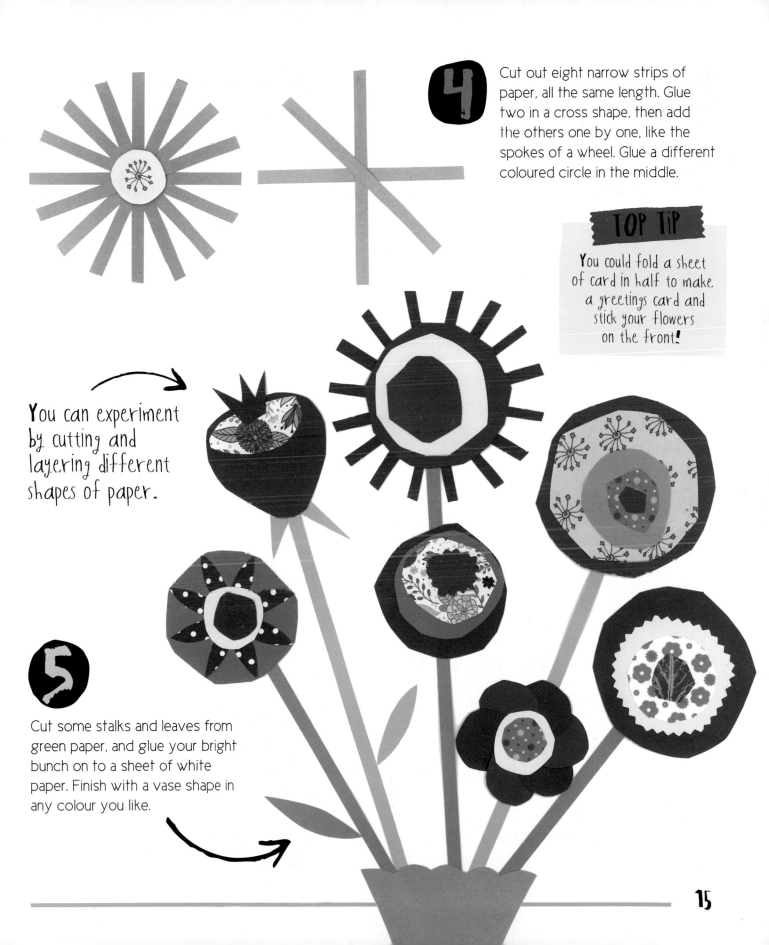

4 Cut out eight narrow strips of paper, all the same length. Glue two in a cross shape, then add the others one by one, like the spokes of a wheel. Glue a different coloured circle in the middle.

TOP TIP

You could fold a sheet of card in half to make a greetings card and stick your flowers on the front!

You can experiment by cutting and layering different shapes of paper.

5 Cut some stalks and leaves from green paper, and glue your bright bunch on to a sheet of white paper. Finish with a vase shape in any colour you like.

PLAYFUL PENGUINS

Use plain white card or paint an icy white background for these fun footprint penguins.

Make a black footprint on a piece of white card or paper, and let it dry.

2

Use a paintbrush to paint two black wings. Paint two white dots for eyes. Cut a triangle from orange paper and stick it on for a beak.

Use a sponge to paint on a white belly.

3 You can make a handprint into a sledging penguin. Keep your fingers and thumb together when you print.

Paint on a head and add a beak and eyes as above.

This slope is cut from blue paper, with white paint dabbed on it using a sponge.

16

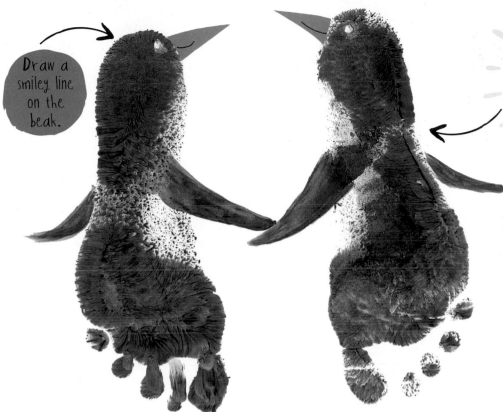

Draw a smiley line on the beak.

Use both feet to make a pair of skipping penguins!

Here's something else you can try ... Draw around your hand on white paper. Cut it out and stick it on to blue card. Now turn each finger into a penguin on an ice block

Paint the bodies and stick on orange beaks and feet.

RAGBAG ROBOTS

Print a rabble of robots using household bits and bobs!

Look around your home for things that could be interesting to make prints of. Here are some ideas. Practise making prints on rough paper first.

Bottle tops

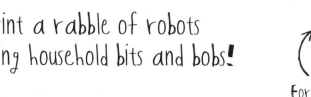
Fork

Staples, pencil sharpeners and pen lids

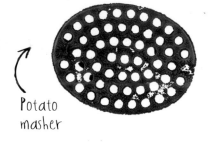
Potato masher

Slotted spatula

Wiggly pasta

Rim of margarine tub

TRY A ROBOT!

Decide which shapes would suit different parts of a robot, then print them together on a sheet of white paper.

Add details using smaller items.

Start with the head and body.

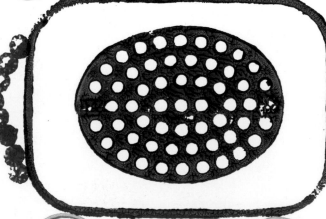

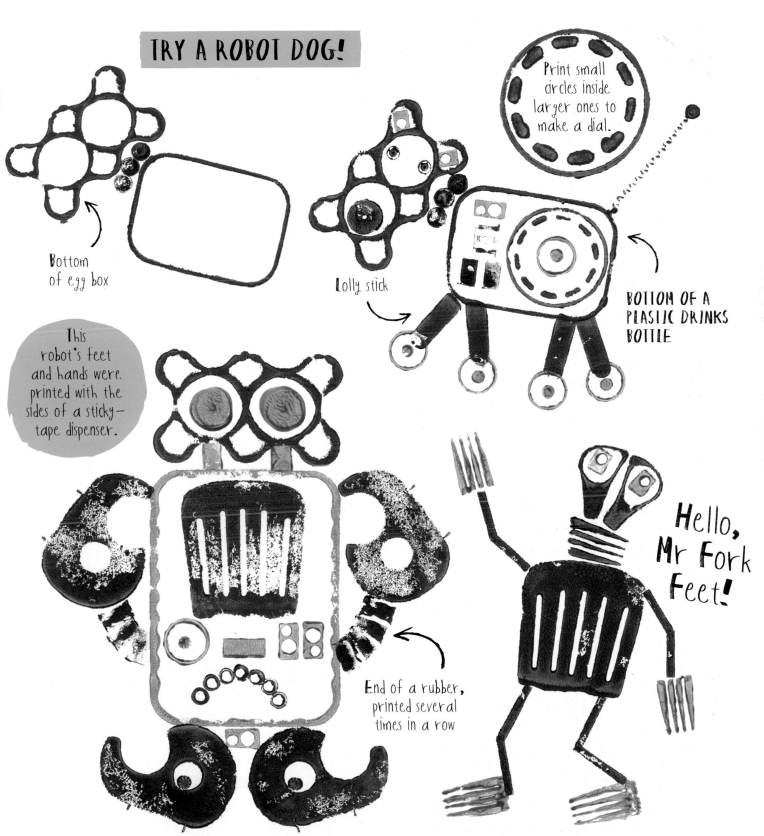

TRY A ROBOT DOG!

Print small circles inside larger ones to make a dial.

Bottom of egg box

Lolly stick

BOTTOM OF A PLASTIC DRINKS BOTTLE

This robot's feet and hands were printed with the sides of a sticky-tape dispenser.

End of a rubber, printed several times in a row

Hello, Mr Fork Feet!

BRILLIANT BALLOONS

Use scraps of old fabric, felt or kitchen cloths to make this hot-air-balloon collage!

1 Start by making a balloon template. Fold a piece of paper, about A5 size, in half. Draw a shape like this by the folded edge.

Cut around the shape and open it out like this to make a template.

2 Cut several strips of fabric, a bit longer than the template's width. Glue them in stripes on to another piece of paper, until you have a block that's as tall as the template.

3 Draw around your template onto the fabric block and cut out the balloon shape. Glue it on to a piece of white paper.

Fingerprint a person to go in the basket.

4 Now make the basket. Cut a shape from fabric and glue it about 2 cm below the balloon. Stick two pieces of thread or wool between the two.

Cut square pieces of fabric and arrange them in a block. Stick them on to paper before cutting out the balloon, as you did in Step 2.

You can cut fancy edges with zigzag craft scissors.

Add a face, hair and some waving arms to your person!

TOP TIP

Thumbprint some birds then draw on beaks, wings and tails. You could stick fabric clouds above them and draw lines to make them look as if they're dangling!

This bush was cut from an old sock.

21

DANGLY DRAGONS

Use scraps of coloured card or packaging to make these friendly fire-breathers.

These little circles of paper came out of a hole punch.

1 Cut out a triangle for the head, about 5 cm wide at the top. There's a template on p.109 if you need it.

2 Glue the triangle on to a piece of scrap paper, then stick on smaller shapes like these ones to create a face. Cut the whole thing out.

3 Cut out an arrow shape for the tail, and lots of narrow strips, 7 or 8 cm long, for the body. Make some straight and others wiggly or spiky.

4 Find a piece of ribbon or wool and lay it on a sheet of newspaper. Dot glue all along it. Stick the strips crossways, so the ribbon lies in the middle. Cut off any spare ribbon at the ends and glue the tail to one end and the head to the other.

TOP TIP
You can dangle your dragon by its tail, or pin it to a wall or pinboard.

THUMBPRINT CIRCUS

Coloured ink pads are useful for making these lively circus characters.

Draw a trapeze for the circus performer to swing from!

1 You can start with just one thumbprint, like this. Draw a face near the top in black pen. Draw stick arms and legs. For the clothes, use colouring pencils or felt-tip pens.

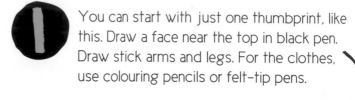

2 Make a thumbprint, then add three fingerprint dots using the tip of your finger. Draw a frilly bottom and colour in the tutu top.

3 Make a thumbprint body. For the head, use the tip of your thumb to make a round print.

4 This horse has a thumbprint body and a fingerprint head.

24

Fingertip print some balloons!

You could add some faces in the crowd.

5 Try making a whole circus scene! Print the performers first, then paint or colour in a yellow circus ring and some big-top stripes around them.

SPONGY WRAP

Use a triangle cut from an everyday sponge to print your own wrapping paper.

1 Cut a triangle shape from a rectangular kitchen sponge. Dip this in paint and practise making prints with it like this:

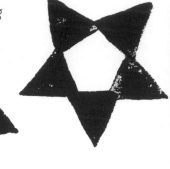

Four triangles in a cross shape, or five triangles in a star

Four triangles with points in the middle

Two triangles with points together

Two triangles with sides together

Rows of triangles

Tear a small piece of sponge to print a blob in the middle of a bow.

2 Now try repeating the pattern all over a sheet of paper. When it's dry, you can use it to wrap presents!

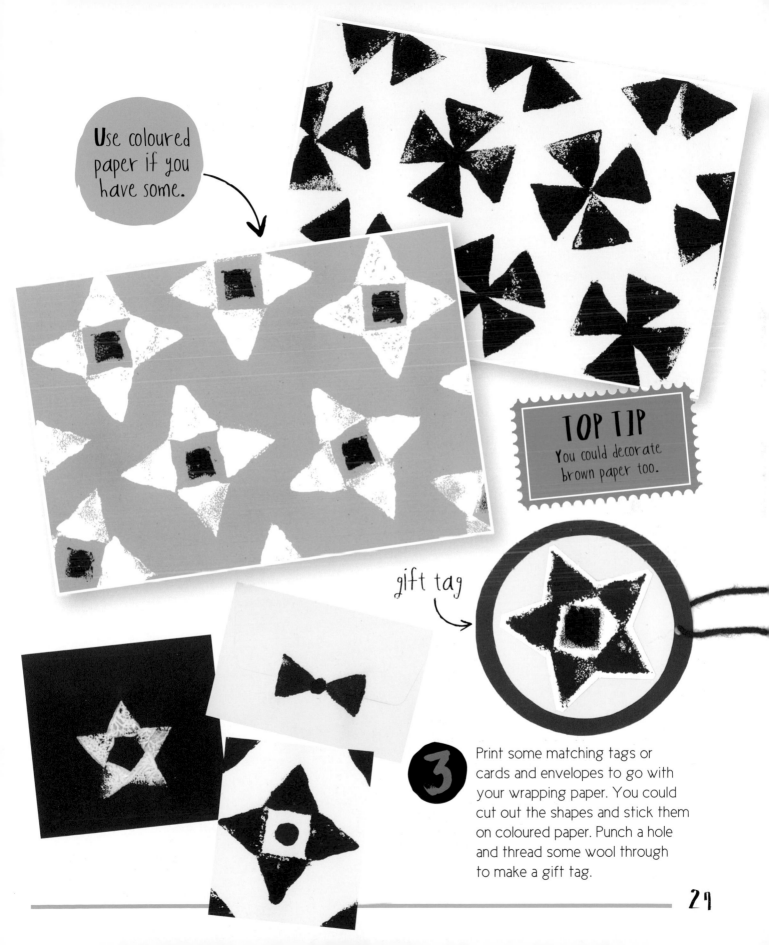

Use coloured paper if you have some.

TOP TIP
You could decorate brown paper too.

gift tag

3 Print some matching tags or cards and envelopes to go with your wrapping paper. You could cut out the shapes and stick them on coloured paper. Punch a hole and thread some wool through to make a gift tag.

ICE-CREAM BUNTING

Recycle card packaging into a delicious decoration! Old cereal packets work well for this project.

THERE ARE TEMPLATES ON P.110 IF YOU NEED THEM!

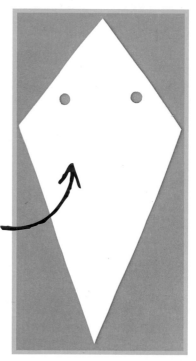

Draw a diamond shape on a piece of white card. If your card is not white, glue some white paper over it. You'll need at least five or six of these shapes.

2 Cut out the shapes and use a hole punch to make two holes in the top part, like this.

For an ice lolly, cut out a long card lolly stick, then punch a hole in the top of it. Thread the wool through, then glue a stripy lolly shape on top.

Why not make a chocolate flake or a cherry?

3 Mix some yellow paint with a little flour or white glue to thicken it. Use this to paint the cones. While the paint is wet, scratch patterns into it using the end of your brush.

4 Cut out some ice-cream shapes from white card – one for each cone. Paint them with thickened paint, as in Step 3. Swirl patterns into the paint. You could scatter on glitter or even real sugar sprinkles to decorate!

5 When the paint is dry, thread your cones on to a long piece of wool or string. Space them out and glue an ice-cream shape over each cone.

Try using nail polish for a drizzle of sauce.

Your bunting is ready to hang!

SWIRLY SNAIL

Wrapping paper and wallpaper scraps work well for this smiley snail.

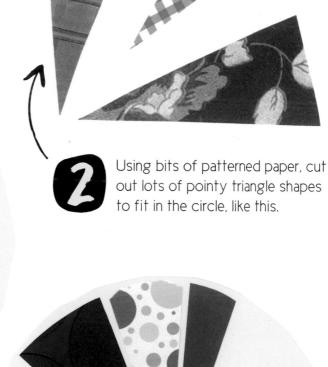

1 Roughly cut out a circle from plain-coloured paper, about the size of a small plate or bowl. This will be the background for the snail's shell.

2 Using bits of patterned paper, cut out lots of pointy triangle shapes to fit in the circle, like this.

3 Arrange the triangles with the points in the middle of the circle, and glue them down.

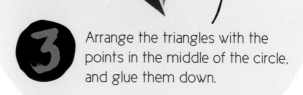

A black-and-white snail made from newspaper is fun to do, too.

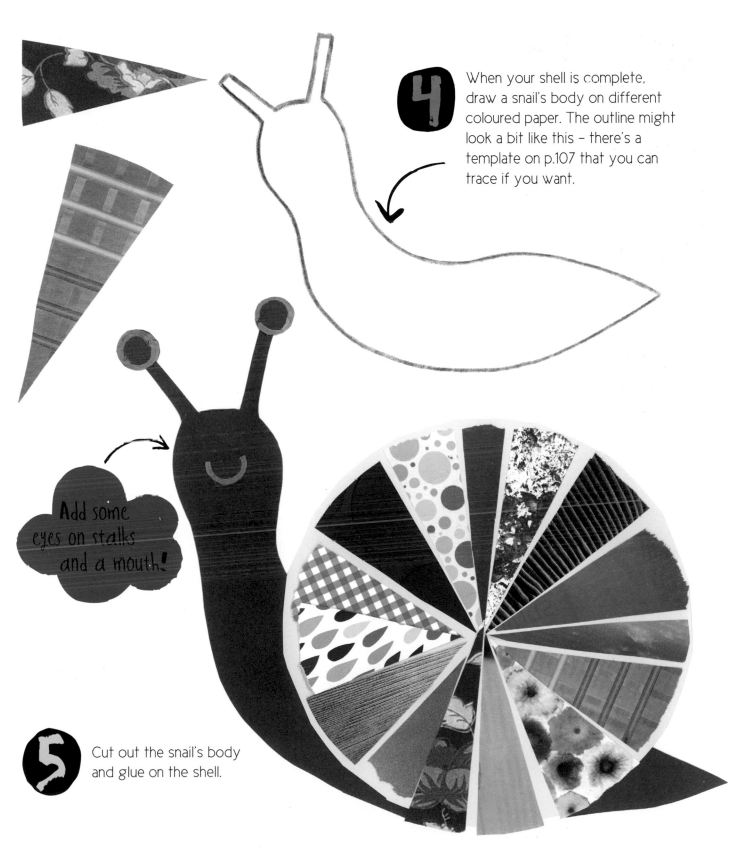

4 When your shell is complete, draw a snail's body on different coloured paper. The outline might look a bit like this – there's a template on p.107 that you can trace if you want.

Add some eyes on stalks and a mouth!

5 Cut out the snail's body and glue on the shell.

PROUD PEACOCK

Turn a hand stencil into a beautiful bird picture!

1 To make the stencil, draw around your hand on thin cardboard. Cut it out, keeping the outside part whole.

2 Lay the stencil over white card or paper. Use a sponge to dab light blue paint over the hand shape.

3 When the paint is dry, lay the stencil back on the paper so the fingers of the stencil are between the fingers of the blue hand. Dab dark blue paint into the stencil fingers.

Draw on the eye, head feathers and legs.

4 Dip your finger in the dark blue paint and use it to paint the peacock's body.

Cut out a yellow paper triangle to make a beak.

32

5 For the tail tips, make lots of green and yellow thumbprints on a piece of white paper. Add fingerprint dots in a different colour on top.

Cut out the tail tips and glue them to your peacock.

You could try a sideways peacock, like this one!

VEGGIE JAM

Create a traffic jam of vehicles with vegetable-print wheels!

1 Ask an adult to help you cut vegetables to give a flat surface. Dry the surface with kitchen paper, dip it in paint and practise making some prints like these.

Onion

Carrot

Mushroom with the stalk removed

2 For a car like this, print two mushroom wheels. Cut a piece from half a pepper to print the roof.

3 When the prints are dry, draw the car's outline and colour it in.

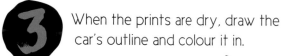

Cut a rectangle of potato to print windows like this.

4 For a bus, start with three onion-print wheels and let them dry. Draw the outline, then add some windows.

These people began as small carrot prints. Draw on a face, hair and shoulders when the paint is dry.

KITCHEN CROCS

Paint kitchen paper to make this super-scaly crocodile collage!

 Lay a sheet of kitchen paper on some newspaper. Use thin, watery paint to colour the kitchen paper green and yellow. Leave it to dry.

The colours will run into each other like this!

 When the paper is dry, cut out or tear shapes like these for a crocodile.

 Glue the shapes on to a piece of white paper. Paint on two white eyes with black dots in the middle. You could tear some small strips from the leftover green kitchen paper and glue them to the tail to make stripes.

Add some paper claws if you like.

Try painting some more sheets of kitchen paper in different colours. When they're dry, tear strips of blue for a lake, and stick them near your crocodile's feet.

You could cut out and stick on some birds, reeds and lilies. There are some templates on p.108 if you need them.

Why not add a swimming croc in the lake?

BIRDS IN BOOTS

Create a **FLOCK** of birds wearing colourful welly boots!

1 Practise drawing bird shapes like these, with a rounded head and a pointed tail. Draw some on to scrap paper and cut them out.

2 Glue your bird shapes on to white paper and draw around them. Cut out wing and beak shapes and stick them on. Draw two legs and an eye.

Why not try making a hen, a duck, a parrot?

YOU COULD ADD SOME SWIRLY TAIL FEATHERS.

3 Cut out some boot shapes from spare wrapping paper or wallpaper, or paint your own patterns.

Now dress up your birds in some boots!

4 Glue the boots over the ends of your birds' legs.

This kitchen cloth makes a great puddle.

39

FACES IN A CROWD

You can have fun with thumbprint faces! Coloured ink pads and felt tips work well for this.

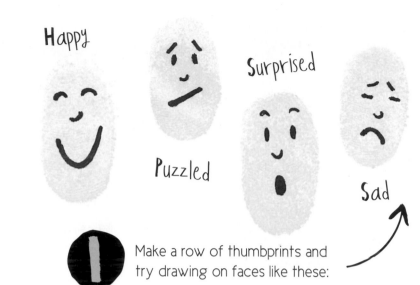

Happy

Puzzled

Surprised

Sad

1 Make a row of thumbprints and try drawing on faces like these:

2 Practise drawing different hairstyles.

A round mouth for a yawn.

You can **ADD** plaits or curls, handbags or headphones!

3 You can draw a neck and shoulders, or add a body using more thumbprints.

There's a cat up a tree!

These people are looking over a fingerprint wall.

4 Make a collection of faces in a crowd scene.

Are some people in a hurry? Where are they going? Think up a story to go with your scene!

SPLAT A CATERPILLAR

Print these cute caterpillars using the end of a balloon!

1 Blow up a long balloon and knot the end. Hold on to the knot, dip the opposite end in some paint and press it on to paper. The harder you press, the bigger the printed blob will be.

2 Print a row of blobs to create a long or wiggly caterpillar. Dip the balloon in more paint each time. Press a bit harder to make the head bigger than the other blobs.

Draw some legs, a mouth and antennae too.

3 Paint two white spots on the head for eyes. When the paint is dry, draw on two black dots with a felt-tip pen.

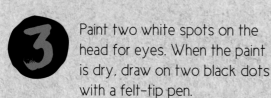

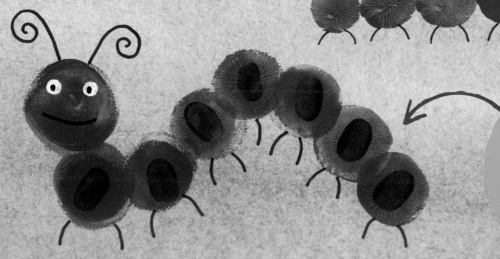

You could thumbprint some spots on your caterpillar!

42

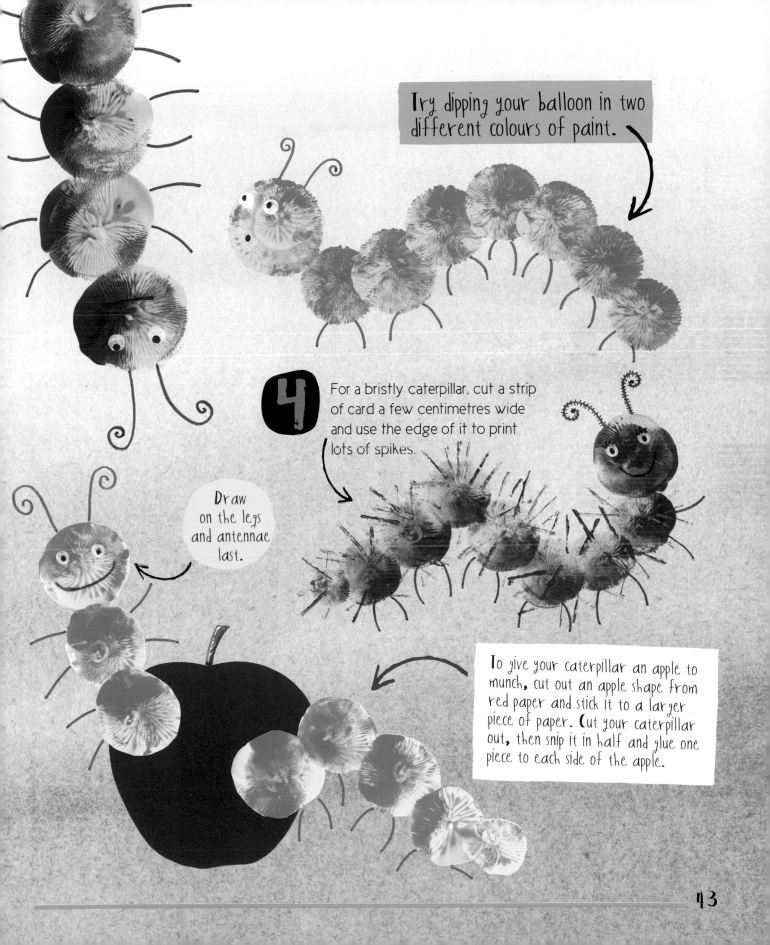

Try dipping your balloon in two different colours of paint.

4 For a bristly caterpillar, cut a strip of card a few centimetres wide and use the edge of it to print lots of spikes.

Draw on the legs and antennae last.

To give your caterpillar an apple to munch, cut out an apple shape from red paper and stick it to a larger piece of paper. Cut your caterpillar out, then snip it in half and glue one piece to each side of the apple.

SOAPY SOLAR SYSTEM

Mix watery paint with soap and salt, to make a picture that's out of this world!

1 Rub a bar of soap back and forth over a piece of white card or paper. Brush watery paint over the top and leave it to dry. You'll get a streaky effect like this:

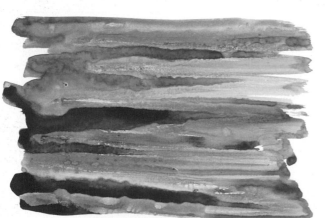

2 For a speckled effect, sprinkle salt over the wet paint and brush it off when dry.

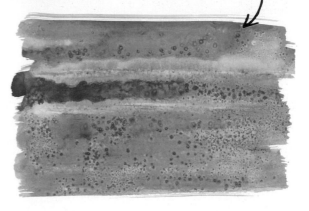

3 When the paint is dry, draw around a cup and cut out circles for planets.

Cut a strip like this and stick it across a planet for a ring.

You could use zigzag craft scissors to make a fiery sun or stars.

While the paint is drying, repeat Step 1 in a few different colours and paint the background for Step 4.

4 For your spacey background, swirl the bar of soap in a spiral over a large sheet of white card or paper. Brush watery dark blue paint all over it and let it dry.

Glue on your planets, stars and sun. You could add an alien or a shooting star!

FRUIT TROOP

A few simple shapes can make a **PRETTY** pattern!

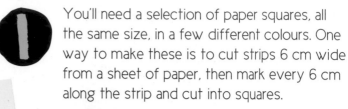

1 You'll need a selection of paper squares, all the same size, in a few different colours. One way to make these is to cut strips 6 cm wide from a sheet of paper, then mark every 6 cm along the strip and cut into squares.

2 On each square, draw a simple fruit shape. The stalk of the fruit should come right to one edge of the square.

3 Carefully cut all around the fruit, starting from the stalk. Keep both the inside and the outside piece whole. When you've cut out one piece of fruit, you can draw around it on a different coloured square!

Leaves can be fiddly to cut, so leave them out if you want to make it easier.

4 Arrange your fruit shapes on a big sheet of dark-coloured paper. Put an outside piece next to an inside piece, and so on. Build up a colourful block. Try putting some pieces upside down or sideways.

When you're happy with your design, glue the pieces down. You could display the picture in your kitchen.

FAST FEET

Turn your footprints into speedy vehicles!

RACING CAR

 Make a coloured footprint and let it dry.

 YOU CAN USE THE TEMPLATES ON P.108 TO HELP YOU.

 Cut out shapes for the wheels, spoiler and driver's helmet.

 On a separate piece of paper, make a thumbprint and draw on a face. Cut this out and stick it on to the helmet.

AEROPLANE

1 Make a coloured footprint and leave it to dry.

2 Stick on coloured paper shapes for the wings and tail.

TOP TIP

To get a clear print, don't move your foot when you're making a footprint.

3 Add some rows of windows – you could draw or paint them on, or use fingerprints to add them in!

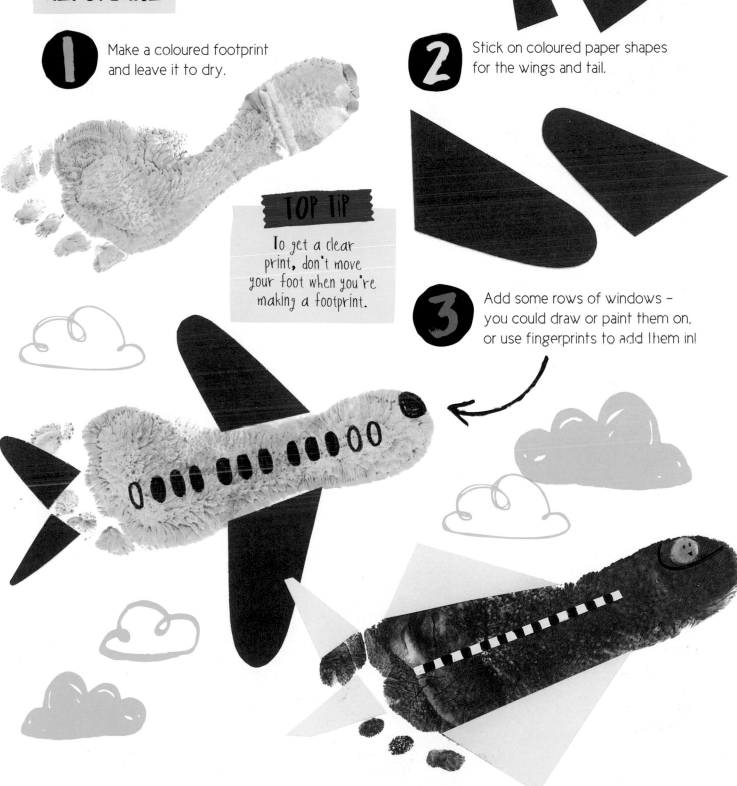

49

SPOTS AND STRIPES

These dangly decorations look lovely hanging on a wall.

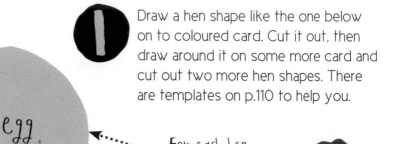

egg

wing

hen

1 Draw a hen shape like the one below on to coloured card. Cut it out, then draw around it on some more card and cut out two more hen shapes. There are templates on p.110 to help you.

For each hen, cut out a wing and an egg in a different colour.

2 Now decorate half of your shapes with spots and half with stripes. To make stripes, lay your cut-out on scrap paper. Cover the edge of a ruler in white paint, then press it across the cut-out. Repeat, spacing the lines a little apart.

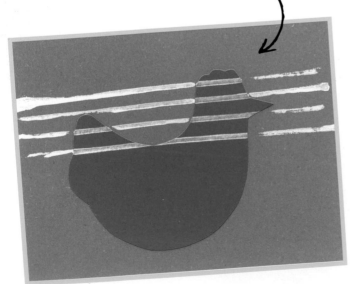

You could try different spaces between the stripes, or make the stripes go from top to bottom.

 For spots, print with the end of a pencil or the rim of a pen lid.

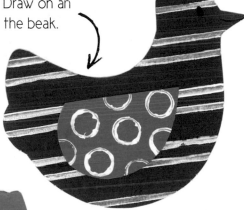

 When everything is dry, glue a wing on to each hen. Draw on an eye and a line across the beak.

Make a loop at the top for hanging.

5 Lay your cut-outs face down in a line, with an egg below each hen. Cut a piece of wool, ribbon or string that reaches from top to bottom and tape it to the back of each shape.

Turn the shapes over and your dangly decoration is complete!

KEY CARTOONS

Use keys to make these prints, then turn them into quirky cartoon characters.

1 Ask an adult for a spare key that you can use. Press it on to a coloured ink pad, then print it on white paper.

2 Try making two key prints with the narrow ends together.

They could become a face ...

3 For a dog, draw a circle with a loop on top, like this.

THERE ARE TEMPLATES ON P.109 IF YOU NEED THEM.

Scribble the ears and neck, and draw in eyes and a smiley mouth.

... or an owl!

52

EXPERIMENT!

What other cartoons
can you create?

MAKE A BIRD

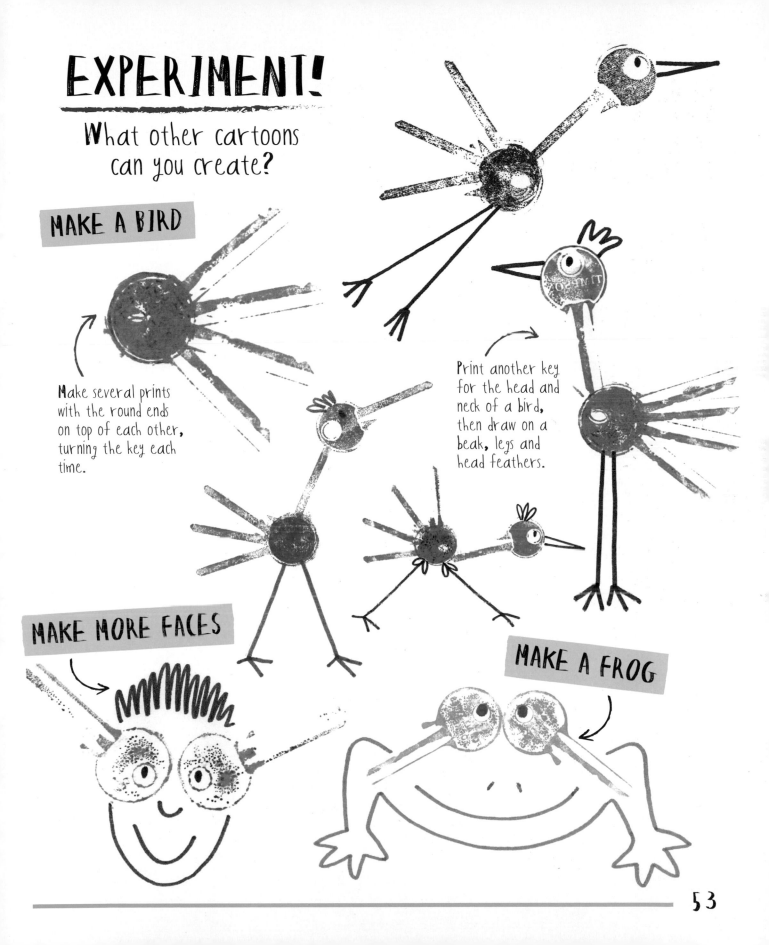

Make several prints
with the round ends
on top of each other,
turning the key each
time.

Print another key
for the head and
neck of a bird,
then draw on a
beak, legs and
head feathers.

MAKE MORE FACES

MAKE A FROG

NOSY BOOKMARKS

THERE ARE TEMPLATES ON P.106 IF YOU NEED.

cardboard envelopes make a great base for these nosy animals. Slot them over a page in your book, with the nose peering down to mark your place.

1 Think of an animal with a long nose or snout, and draw the outline of its head on to card.

An elephant might look like this!

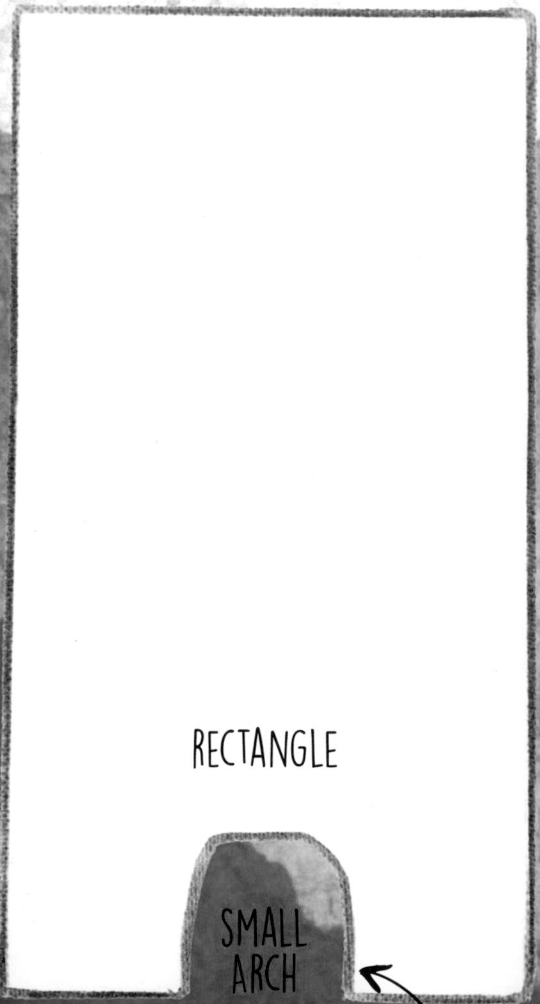

RECTANGLE

SMALL ARCH

2 Cut out the head shape, then cut a rectangle for the body with a small arch between the legs, like this.

54

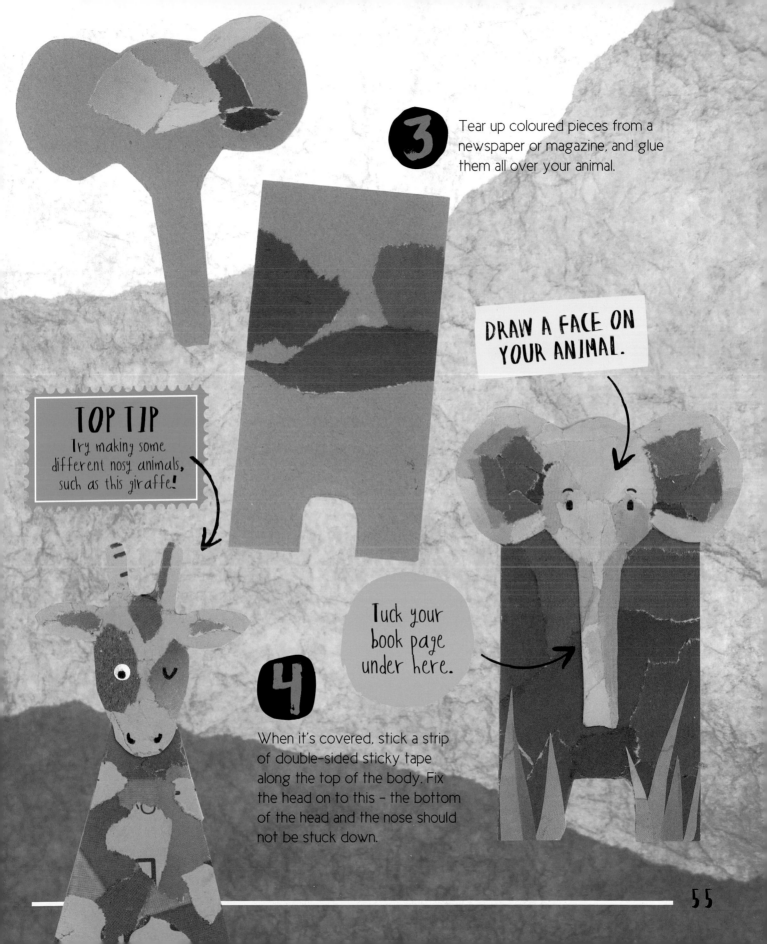

3 Tear up coloured pieces from a newspaper or magazine, and glue them all over your animal.

DRAW A FACE ON YOUR ANIMAL.

TOP TIP
Try making some different nosy animals, such as this giraffe!

Tuck your book page under here.

4 When it's covered, stick a strip of double-sided sticky tape along the top of the body. Fix the head on to this – the bottom of the head and the nose should not be stuck down.

HANDY DINOSAURS

Make your hands into different shapes to create these bright beasties!

1 Spread out your fingers and thumb, and draw around your hand. Cut out and glue on a tail shape.

This white eye was punched from a hole punch! Draw on a black dot and glue it down.

Add triangles for the spikes and beak.

TOP TIP

For each one of these dinosaurs, draw around your hand on coloured paper, as shown in the outlines. Cut it out and stick it on to a paper or card background, then stick on the dinosaur features.

2 Curl your hand into a fist but leave your thumb pointing out. Draw around your hand. Cut out the handprint, and stick it on to a piece of paper.

Cut out shapes for the legs, tail and spikes. Stick them down.

Draw on a smiley face.

3 Rest your hand on its side with the fingers together and the thumb below them. The thumb will make the dinosaur's bottom jaw. Cut out the shape you've drawn, and stick it on a piece of paper. Cut out and stick on paper shapes for the eye, teeth and cheek.

Fingerprint some dots on the dinosaur.

4 Put your hand flat and draw around it. Cut out the handprint, and stick it to a piece of paper. Cut out shapes for the neck frill, horns and tail.

Use a hole punch and pen to make the eye and the mouth.

5 Draw around a flat hand on corrugated paper and cut off the finger section. Snip some pink paper to make the flowers, and stick them to each point of the plant.

BUILDING BLOCKS

A small strip of cardboard is all you need to design and print your own building!

CAN YOU BUILD A HOUSE?

PROJECT 1

1. Print four lines to make a square – the sides could be one, two or even three strips long.

One print makes a short line like this.

Join up two prints for a longer line.

2. Print the main walls first, then add a roof, windows, a chimney and a fence. For a door, drag the card strip sideways across the paper to pull the paint into a solid rectangle shape.

CAN YOU BUILD A TALL TOWER?

PROJECT 2

1. Print three lines in a triangle shape at the top.

2. For battlements, cut a shorter strip of card. Print three sides of a square, then turn the corner, as shown.

TEXTURED TURTLES

Make an underwater world by printing from a piece of cling film!

There are templates on p.109.

1 Tear off some cling film at least the size of a piece of A4 paper. Lay it over newspaper, then use a damp sponge to cover it with blue paint. Press a piece of white A4 paper on top, then peel the paper off.

TOP TIP

Try a few prints — you'll get different textures depending on how watery your paint is.

2 While the paper is drying, make a couple more cling-film prints using yellow and green paper. When they are dry, cut out shapes for a turtle – there are templates on p.109.

3 Stick the turtle on to the blue background. You could cut out some oval shapes in a different colour and stick them on the shell, too.

Cling—film print some different coloured paper to make rocks and starfish!

SHADY TREES

You don't need brightly coloured paper to create an eye-catching picture!

Cut a strip of brown parcel paper. Make the edges a bit wobbly, like a tree trunk. Glue it on to a white background.

3 Add shorter, thinner strips for branches, and cut leaf shapes from old newspaper and glue them on.

2 Now cut a narrower strip from a light brown envelope, the same height as your tree trunk. Stick this down one side of the trunk, to give the effect of light shining on it.

Try cutting out or drawing some animals to hide among your trees. The dark colours here were cut out from old magazines.

TOP TIP

If you make a tree the whole height of your paper, it will seem closer than the others.

4 You can create a shadow on the ground by cutting a strip of brown paper the width of the tree trunk and gluing it at an angle at the bottom of your tree trunk.

FINGERPRINT SWEET SHOP

You can make a whole sweet shop's worth of tasty treats, using just coloured ink, pencils and paper!

1 Start by drawing the outline of a jar.

2 Press your fingertip on to a brightly coloured ink pad and print lots of dots inside the jar. Do one colour, then wipe your finger clean and print another colour.

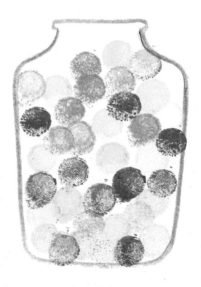

These sweets are made from thumbprints. Draw on the wrappers afterwards.

3 For a lolly, make two thumbprints in a heart shape, or fingerprint some dots in a circle. Draw on the sticks and an outline if you like.

4 You can turn lots of dots into a cupcake or a sundae! There are some templates on p.108 to help with the bases, if you need.

5 You could make a whole range of sweet treats and cut them out to stick in your own sweet shop.

Use coloured paper for the background, and glue on long, thin strips in a different colour for shelves.

Try making different lids for your jars. You can draw them or cut them from scrap paper.

Try cutting out a cupcake case from old wrapping paper, like this.

POTATO PARROTS

Make your spuds squawk as you print these pretty parrots! You'll need two fairly large potatoes.

1 Ask an adult to help you cut one potato in half lengthways to give a big, oval-shaped flat surface, and the other widthways to give a smaller oval. Dry the surfaces with kitchen paper.

Cover the large piece in yellow paint and print it on white paper. Cover the smaller piece in red paint and print it on top, like this.

2 Cut a wedge from the spare big piece of potato, and use it to print red wings and a tail.

3 When the prints are dry, paint a white face like this on to the parrot's head. Scratch some curved lines into the wet paint using the end of your paintbrush.

Use brown paint and the edge of a strip of card to print a branch. Paint some claws clinging on to it.

4 When the face is dry, paint on a black beak and eyes. You could add some red head feathers, and a grey line down the middle of the beak, too.

To make a flying parrot, print a few strips on each side for flapping wings, and extra strips for the tail.

If you have some old broccoli, you could use it to print green leaves!

This pink cheek was made with a fingerprint.

For a sideways parrot, print the wing strips at the back only.

MONEY TREES

Use a cluster of coin rubbings to make some magical money trees!

 Try to use a mixture of different coins. Lay a piece of thin paper over a coin, and rub a wax crayon on the surface.

TOP TIP

Hold the paper over the coin with one finger, to keep it steady as you work.

 For a brighter effect, brush watery paint over your rubbing. The crayon will resist the paint! Don't worry about neat edges – you're going to cut the coins out.

3 Make lots of colourful rubbings and cut them out. Keep them safe while you paint a white tree trunk and branches on to coloured paper or card. You could scratch lines into the trunk using the end of your brush, to look like bark. Let it dry.

Now glue your paper coins on to your tree, like leaves.

68

HERE ARE SOME OTHER IDEAS YOU CAN TRY ...

LUCKY BOUQUET

Cut strips of green paper for stalks and glue them down. Glue on a piece of doily, then stick a cluster of coins on top. Add two paper triangles and a square for the bow.

TREE IN A TUB

Stick down a cluster of coins. Glue on a trunk shape cut from coloured paper, and a piece of cupcake case for a pot.

Stick all the coin rubbings on to coloured paper or card.

CHRISTMAS TREE

Cut out a green paper triangle and a yellow trunk. Glue on pieces of doily for decoration, and stick the coins on top.

You could fold the paper first, to make a greetings card with a lucky coin tree on the front.

PUPS IN PRINT

Simple torn—up newspaper is perfect for these pups.

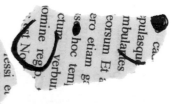

Make your dog a basket or a bone.

1 Tear a big oblong shape for the body and a smaller one for the head. Glue them to some plain paper.

2 Draw on legs, a tail, ears and a face, like these.

3

To make a shaggy dog, draw an outline of the animal in pencil – there are templates on p.107 to help. Then tear up lots of thin strips of newspaper. Glue the top of each strip to the top of the dog and let the rest hang down.

Use strips of coloured newspaper for a bow . . .

Cut **OUT** cloud shapes for a fluffy poodle.

. . . or a collar!

BEES AND BUGS

Turn your finger and thumbprints into a collection of cute creepy crawlies! Squeeze some paint on to a paper plate. Press the pad of your thumb or finger into the paint, then press it on to paper to leave a print.

BUMBLE BEE

1 Make a yellow thumb print. Add two white wings using the tip of your index finger.

2 When the paint has dried, draw on the markings with a black pen.

SPIDER

1 Paint white dots on a dark thumbprint, then draw black dots for the eyes.

2 Add eight legs and a web or dangly thread!

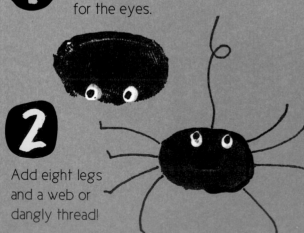

LADYBIRD

1 Make a red thumb print and let it dry.

2 Draw on the ladybird's dots and six legs.

Try adding some curly antennae.

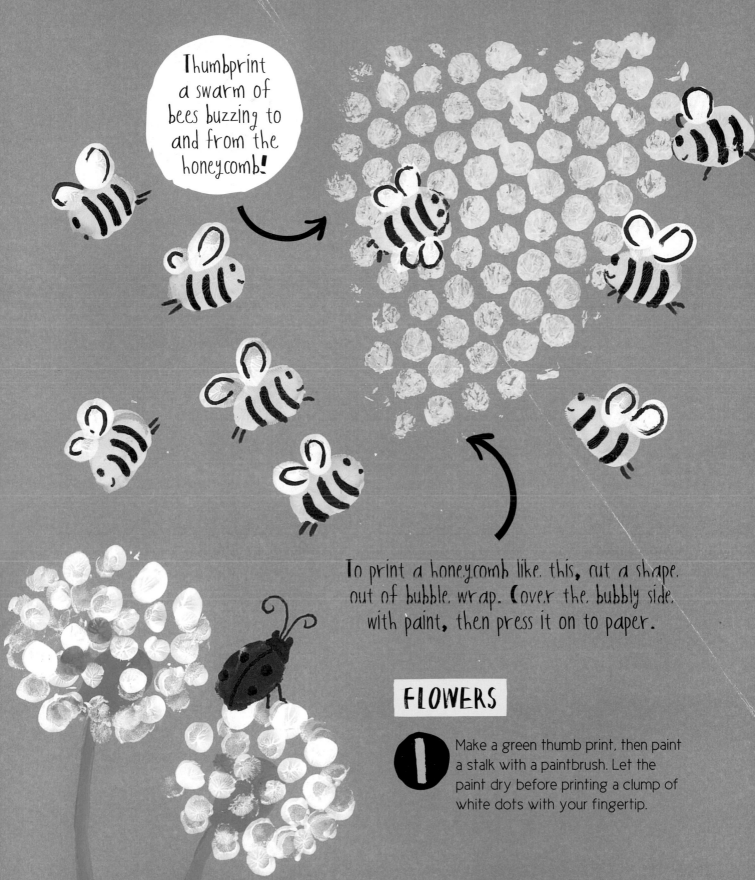

Thumbprint a swarm of bees buzzing to and from the honeycomb!

To print a honeycomb like this, cut a shape out of bubble wrap. Cover the bubbly side with paint, then press it on to paper.

FLOWERS

1. Make a green thumb print, then paint a stalk with a paintbrush. Let the paint dry before printing a clump of white dots with your fingertip.

MONSTER MADNESS

Start with a simple fruit print and see what crazy creatures you can make!

1 Cut a piece of fruit in half, so that one side is flat. Dry the flat surface with kitchen paper, then cover it with paint and press it on to paper. Make a few prints, leaving space around each one.

 Pear

Orange

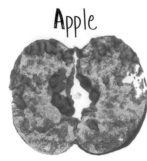 Apple

2 While your prints are drying, cut out some shapes like these from coloured paper. Make them the right size for your prints.

Tail

Antennae

Eyes: stick a circle of white paper on a larger coloured circle and draw on a black dot.

Mouth: stick on white shapes for teeth.

Arms and legs: can be long or short, clawed or webbed!

Spikes and horns

3 Glue the paper shapes to your prints to make monsters!

This two-headed flying monster started with two apple prints.

Let your imagination run wild and make a monster party!

Prints aren't always perfect! Turn gaps into features, like this wide-open mouth.

Stick circles to the ends of two narrow strips for eyes on stalks.

Cut a carrot lengthways for a tall, thin monster like this.

SPONGY SNOWMEN

Use a sponge and a cardboard stencil to paint a flurry of snowman friends.

1 To make the stencil, draw two circles like this on to thin cardboard. You can use cups or rolls of tape as a guide. Cut out the shape, <u>keeping the outside piece whole.</u>

TOP TIP

If you keep the inside piece too, you can use it for the puppet on p.84!

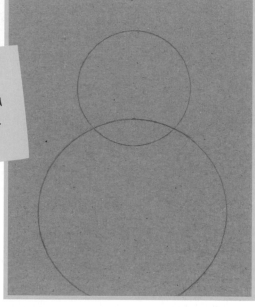

2 Now lay the stencil on a larger piece of cardboard. Dip a sponge in thick white paint and dab it all over the cut-out shape.

3 Use the sponge to paint a line of snow at the bottom. Tear off a small piece of sponge to paint some snowflakes.

4 Cut a strip of sponge and cover one edge in black paint. Press it down to print two arms. Print the eyes and buttons with the end of a pencil, and paint a line of dots for the mouth.

5 Now dress up your snowman! Use your sponge to dab coloured paint on to paper.

Try a clown hat, bow tie or some sunglasses!

Cut out hat and scarf shapes to stick on.

Hat

Scarf

Cut out a triangular nose from orange card or packaging and stick it on.

PEOPLE PYRAMID

You can have lots of fun with simple collage figures. Glue them on to a piece of white paper or card.

1 Cut out some head shapes from scrap paper or magazines. Draw or glue on different faces. Try using lips or ears from a photo! Punch some holes in paper with a hole punch, and use the little circles for eyes or cheeks.

2 Look for patterned paper and try cutting these simple shapes for clothes. You might find fabric textures in a catalogue. Cut strips for arms and legs, and two oval feet.

Cut out hair from photos!

3 When you've practised making people, try piling some up in a pyramid shape! Start with the bottom row, then perch the others on top.

Cut up a paper doily for frilly clothes.

You could add some party hats and bows. This tutu is made from a cupcake case!

HAUNTED HANDS

Make these spooky spooks with white paint on black card, and pin them up to haunt your house for Halloween!

Make a white handprint and let it dry. Use black paint or a marker to add a scary face.

A white footprint can be spooky too.

For this skeleton, make a fist with your thumb tucked in, and dip your bent fingers into the paint. Make a print, then either paint or print on a skull and some arms.

Try drawing different faces on some other ghosts.

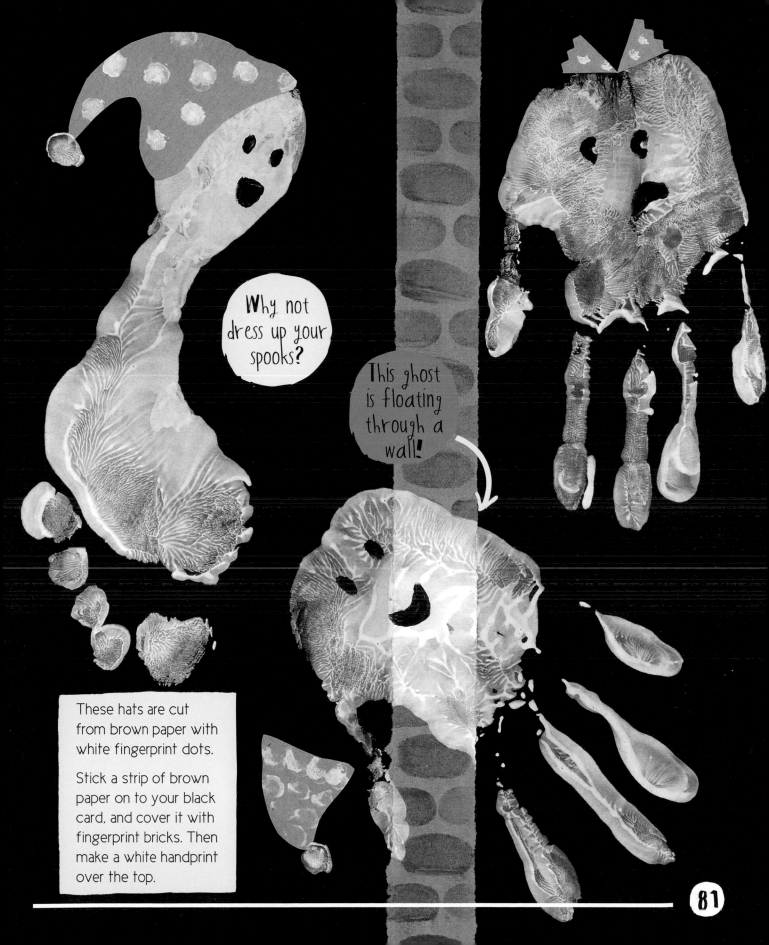

Why not dress up your spooks?

This ghost is floating through a wall!

These hats are cut from brown paper with white fingerprint dots.

Stick a strip of brown paper on to your black card, and cover it with fingerprint bricks. Then make a white handprint over the top.

81

BOTTLE-TOP BALLOONS

You could print these on a piece of folded paper to make a great greetings card!

1 Collect the lids of some old bottles, all of a similar size. Cover the top of a lid in paint and print it on to white paper. Repeat using the other lids and different colours, to create a bright bunch of balloons!

2 Use a felt-tip pen to draw some strings coming down from the balloons.

3 Press your thumb into paint or a coloured ink pad to print a person dangling from the balloons.

Draw on arms, legs, a face and hair!

4 Experiment with different balloons! Print a row of small bottle tops to make a long balloon.

TRY printing with the rim of a bottle top, then fingerprint some dots inside!

TOP TIP

You could dangle an animal from your balloons. Make two thumbprints in the same colour. Then draw on a face, ears, legs and an elephant's trunk or a monkey's curly tail.

Uh-oh, here comes a bird to pop the balloons!

LOLLY-STICK PUPPETS

These puppets are a great way to recycle old food packaging and lolly sticks.

1 Draw two circles like this on a piece of thin cardboard, as you did for the snowman on p.76. Cut out the whole shape.

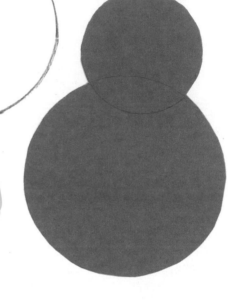

2 Cut a circle of white paper, the same size as the big circle, and paint or stick on red stripes. Glue this on to your cardboard shape.

THERE ARE TEMPLATES ON P.109 IF YOU NEED THEM.

3 Paint or stick on a beard shape. This one was cut from a magazine. Draw on a face with an eyepatch.

4 Cut out a black pirate's hat and paint on white crossbones. Cut out a card hand, hook and boot. Stick each one to a wire freezer-bag tie or pipe cleaner – tape them in place at the back.

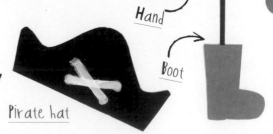

Hook

Hand

Boot

Pirate hat

5 Tape the other end of each arm and leg to the back of the pirate's body. Glue the hat on to the head. You could stick on a sword cut from foil packaging.

WHAT OTHER PUPPET CHARACTERS CAN YOU MAKE?

Tape on a lolly stick for a handle that doubles as a wooden leg!

TRY AN ASTRONAUT

Stick two circles of newspaper on to another cardboard base as before. Decorate with shapes cut from coloured paper and foil.

Make a thumbprint on a small circle of white paper. Draw on a face and stick it on the astronaut's head.

FLIGHTY KITES

Mix and match different papers for a flurry of kites flying high!

1 You can make a kite by sticking four squares of differently coloured paper on to some scrap paper or card. Draw on a diamond shape, as shown, and cut it out.

2 For a round kite, cut out two circles of the same size. Fold one of them in half, then into quarters, and cut along the folds. Glue two of the quarters on to the other whole circle from different coloured papers.

For this kite, arrange triangles in a circle with their narrowest point in the middle.

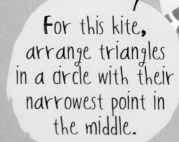

Cut out cloud shapes from old newspaper and scribble over them with white crayon or paint.

Add some colourful flowing tails to your kites, using strips or triangles of paper.

3 Glue everything on to a piece of pale blue card.

DOTTY DELIGHTS

You can make lots of pretty patterns with fingerprint dots! For gift tags or decorations, do this onto small pieces of card. Try some of these patterns. Use a cloth or kitchen paper to wipe your finger when you change colour, or use different fingers for different colours.

PROJECT 1

Start with the middle dot, then surround it with circles of dots in a different colour. Add as many circles as you like.

To make a dot, dip the tip of your finger in paint and dab it lightly on to paper.

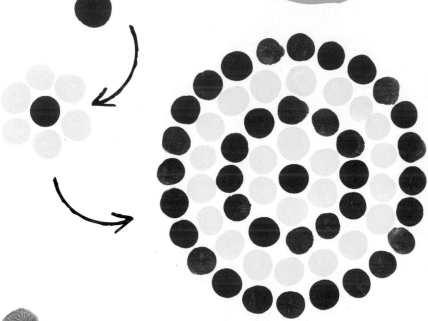

PROJECT 2

For this pattern, start with the middle dot, then add more dots to make a square shape, like this one.

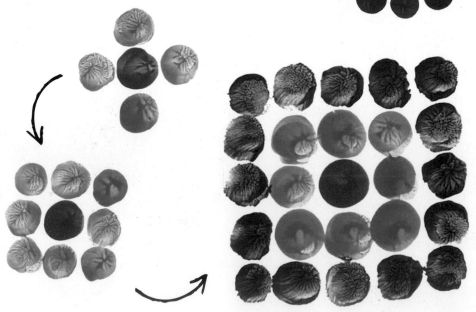

Start with a line of dots, then turn it into a cross. Fill in L–shapes in the corners until you have a complete square.

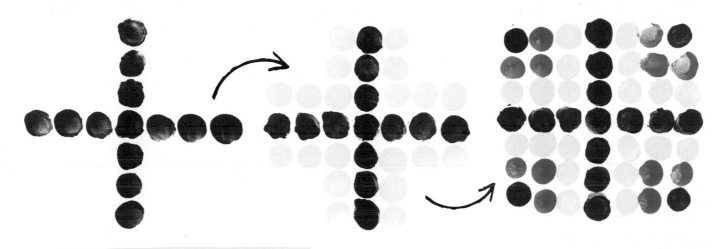

To make a gift tag, cut out your dotty pattern. Make a hole near one edge using a hole punch or darning needle. Thread through some wool or ribbon and knot the ends.

TOP TIP

You could stick your pattern on to coloured card.

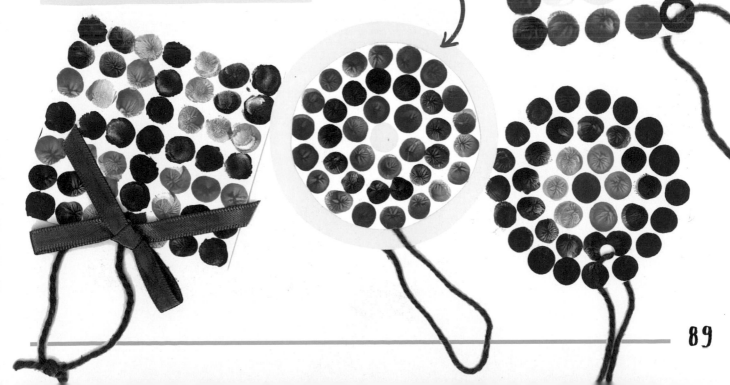

BUBBLY SNAKES

Printing with bubble wrap is a great way to make snaky scales!

1 Cut out a wiggly snake shape from coloured paper or card. Lay it on to newspaper, ready to print.

2 Take a piece of bubble wrap and paint all over the bubbly side, then press this down on to the snake. Repeat until you have covered the whole snake with dots. Let it dry.

3 Cut a narrow strip of bubble wrap and use it to print stripes in a different colour. Draw on a smiley mouth and paint or stick on shapes for the eyes and tongue.

90

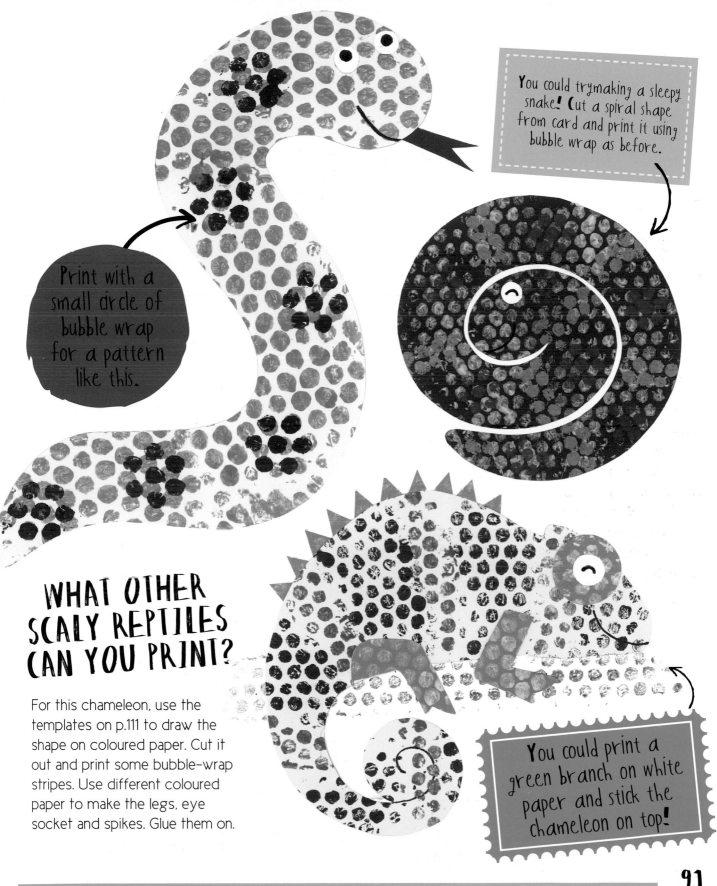

You could try making a sleepy snake! Cut a spiral shape from card and print it using bubble wrap as before.

Print with a small circle of bubble wrap for a pattern like this.

WHAT OTHER SCALY REPTILES CAN YOU PRINT?

For this chameleon, use the templates on p.111 to draw the shape on coloured paper. Cut it out and print some bubble-wrap stripes. Use different coloured paper to make the legs, eye socket and spikes. Glue them on.

You could print a green branch on white paper and stick the chameleon on top!

FLOWERS AND FIREWORKS

Create some bright sparks with the cardboard tube from the middle of a toilet roll!

1. Start by cutting slits up from one end of the tube. The slits should be about 4 cm long and roughly 1 cm apart.

Splay out the split ends, like this.

2. Squeeze some red and yellow paint on to a paper plate. Dip the splayed end of the tube into it and move it around until the strips are all coated. Press the tube on to paper, and you'll get a shape like this.

3. You could turn your pattern into a flower or a sun. Use your fingertip to print dots in the middle. Paint in a stalk and leaves, or cut them from green paper and glue them on.

WOVEN WALLS

Weave windows into some papery city walls!

Weave these in and out through the slits.

1 Fold a rectangle of paper – about half the width of a piece of A4 – in half, lengthways. Mark lines across from the folded edge, spacing them about 3 cm apart. Stop each line about a centimetre from the opposite edge. Cut along the lines and open the paper out.

3 CM

◄ 1CM ►

2 From a different coloured paper, cut out some strips the same height as your rectangle and about 2 cm wide.

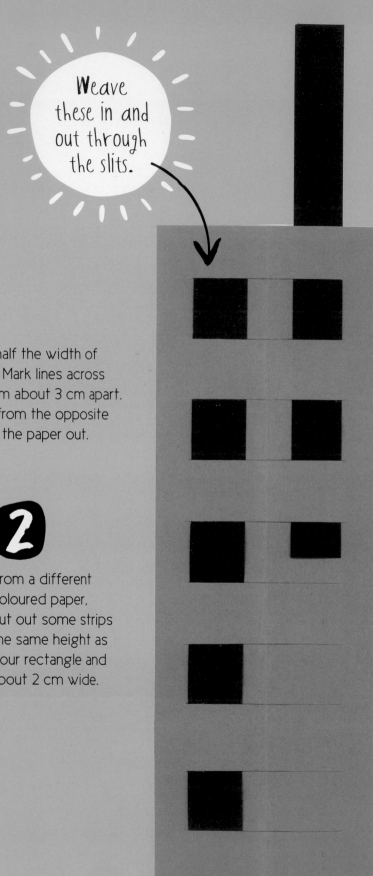

FIST-PRINT FISH

Clench your fist to make a whole shoal of these fantastic fish!

1 Hold your fist with your palm facing downwards and your thumb tucked in, and dip your bent fingers into some paint. Press your fist onto white paper, making sure you don't print the bottom of your palm, too.

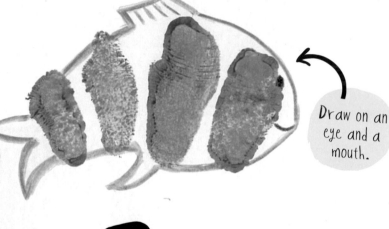

2 When the print is dry, draw the outline of a fish around it, like this.

Draw on an eye and a mouth.

3 Try two colours! Print a yellow fist and let it dry. Then clean your hand, dip it in another colour and print a pink fist over the top, in the gaps.

4 For this fish, print one fist above another.

Make the tail and bottom fin from thumbprints.

5 Try making a handprint jellyfish! Keep your fingers and thumb pressed together. Fingerprint some dots in a different colour on top, and paint on a face.

TOP TIP

You could print some weeds using your fingers.

This fish is a handprint, like the jellyfish.

Make some fingertip prints for bubbles

97

STAMP
INTO
SPACE

Send your footprint into orbit by turning it into a space rocket!

You'll need a sheet of dark blue or black paper. Paint the bottom of your foot white, and your toes orange. Tread firmly on the paper, keeping your foot still to make a print. Lift your foot off carefully and wipe it clean.

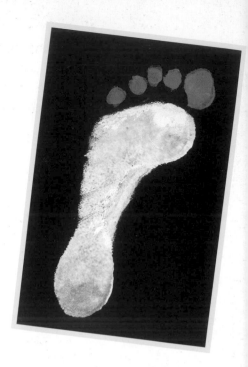

2 When your footprint is dry, lay it on newspaper. Add a little water to some yellow paint in a cup. Use a paintbrush to splatter-paint some stars. Ideally do this outside!

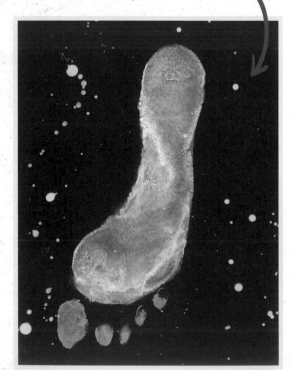

3 To make the nose, tail and decoration for your rocket, cut out shapes like these from coloured paper. Make sure you make them the right size for your footprint.

4 Glue the paper shapes on to your rocket. In the porthole, make a thumbprint and draw on an astronaut's face.

Make an Earth print in the same way as the moon, but use a larger cardboard circle and add some white and green paint too. Print it on to light blue paper and cut it out.

5 To make a moon, draw a circle on to cardboard and cut it out. Sponge white paint unevenly all over it, then press it on to dark-coloured paper to make a print.

PATCHWORK PATTERNS

You can make rubbings from all sorts of everyday items and turn them into beautiful designs.

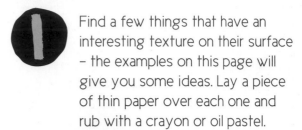

Find a few things that have an interesting texture on their surface – the examples on this page will give you some ideas. Lay a piece of thin paper over each one and rub with a crayon or oil pastel.

These patterns came from the different sides of a cheese grater.

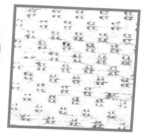

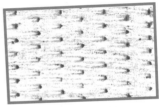

FOR STRIPES TRY:

Corrugated card

A griddle pan

A slotted spatula

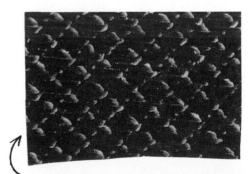

Try rubbing gently on coloured tissue paper

The bottom of a shoe

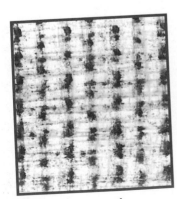

A mesh bag

Patterns on carved furniture, belt buckles or trinkets

2 Make a selection of rubbings, then cut out squares, rectangles, circles and triangles from them. Arrange them in patterns and glue them on to scrap paper or card.

Try making a postcard!

Cut strips of a similar width and arrange them around a picture, like a frame!

Smaller shapes make great gift tags or bookmarks.

You could tape a cocktail stick or skewer to the back, for a fun flag decoration.

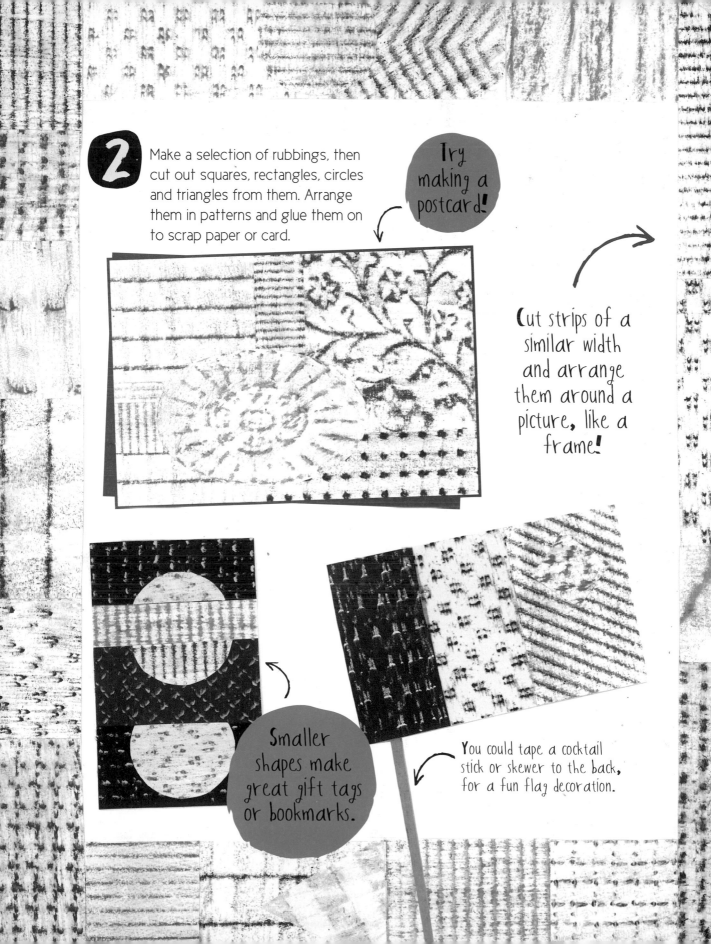

PRINTED PUFFERFISH

You can use paint or ink pads to fingerprint these fun fish!

1 Draw around a bowl on a piece of white paper and cut out the circle. Cut out three coloured paper shapes like this for a tail and fins.

2 Fingerprint dots all over the white circle – try using two different colours.

3 Arrange the shapes on a sheet of blue paper, to make a fish.

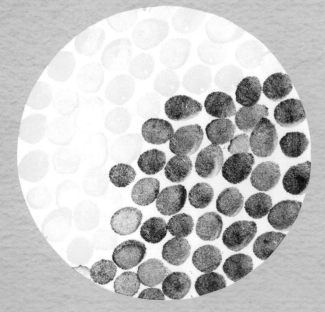

Dip the end of a ruler into some paint and use it to print lots of spines on your fish.

Draw on a face.

Try printing some different coloured puffer fish. You could stick on some pink paper heart shapes to make a **V**alentine's card!

UMBRELLA PARADE

Use wrapping paper, wallpaper or even colourful magazine pages for this cheery rainy-day collage!

Dip a sponge in pale-blue paint and dab it on to a sheet of white A3 card for a cloudy effect.

While the paint is drying, draw around a large glass on a piece of patterned paper and cut out the circle. Draw a wavy line across it, like this.

Cut along the scalloped line to give an umbrella shape.

Make some more umbrellas in the same way – try different shapes and sizes by changing the thing you draw around and the position of the wavy line, and different patterned papers.

Cut out some pieces like this for a person beneath an umbrella.

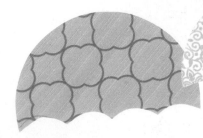

6 Now glue your umbrellas on to the cloudy background! Start at the top and finish with people at the bottom.

Draw on handles with a felt pen.

For a front-on umbrella, use a whole paper circle and draw on some spokes.

Water down some blue paint and splatter it on to your collage!

TEMPLATES

BATS
P.6—9

ANIMAL BODIES
P.54—55

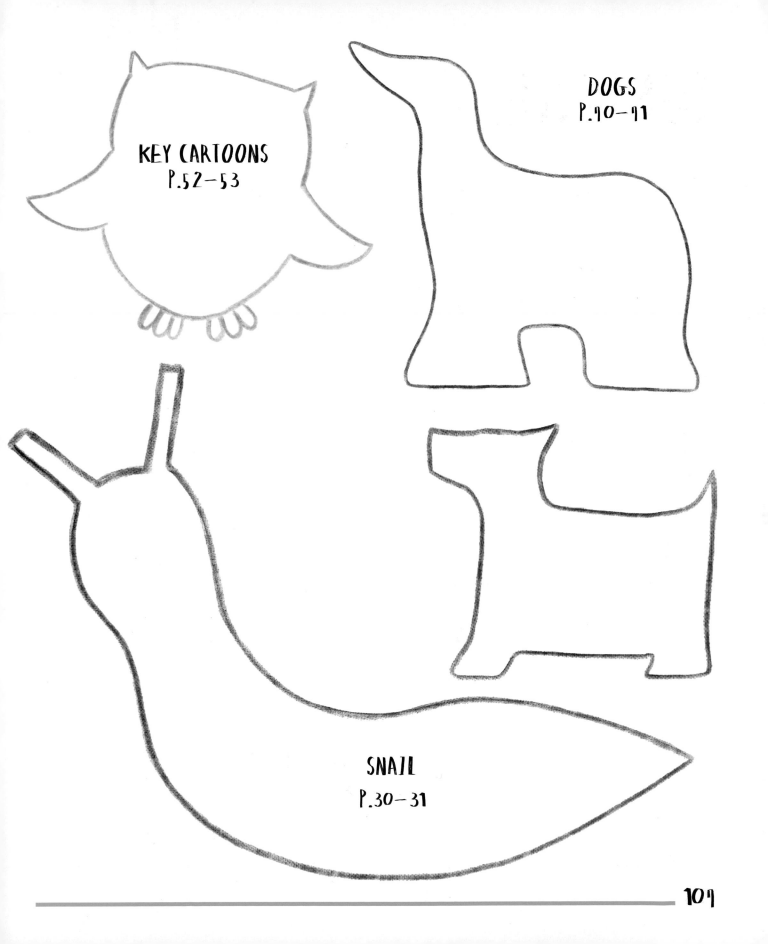

KEY CARTOONS
P.52—53

DOGS
P.90—91

SNAIL
P.30—31

TEMPLATES

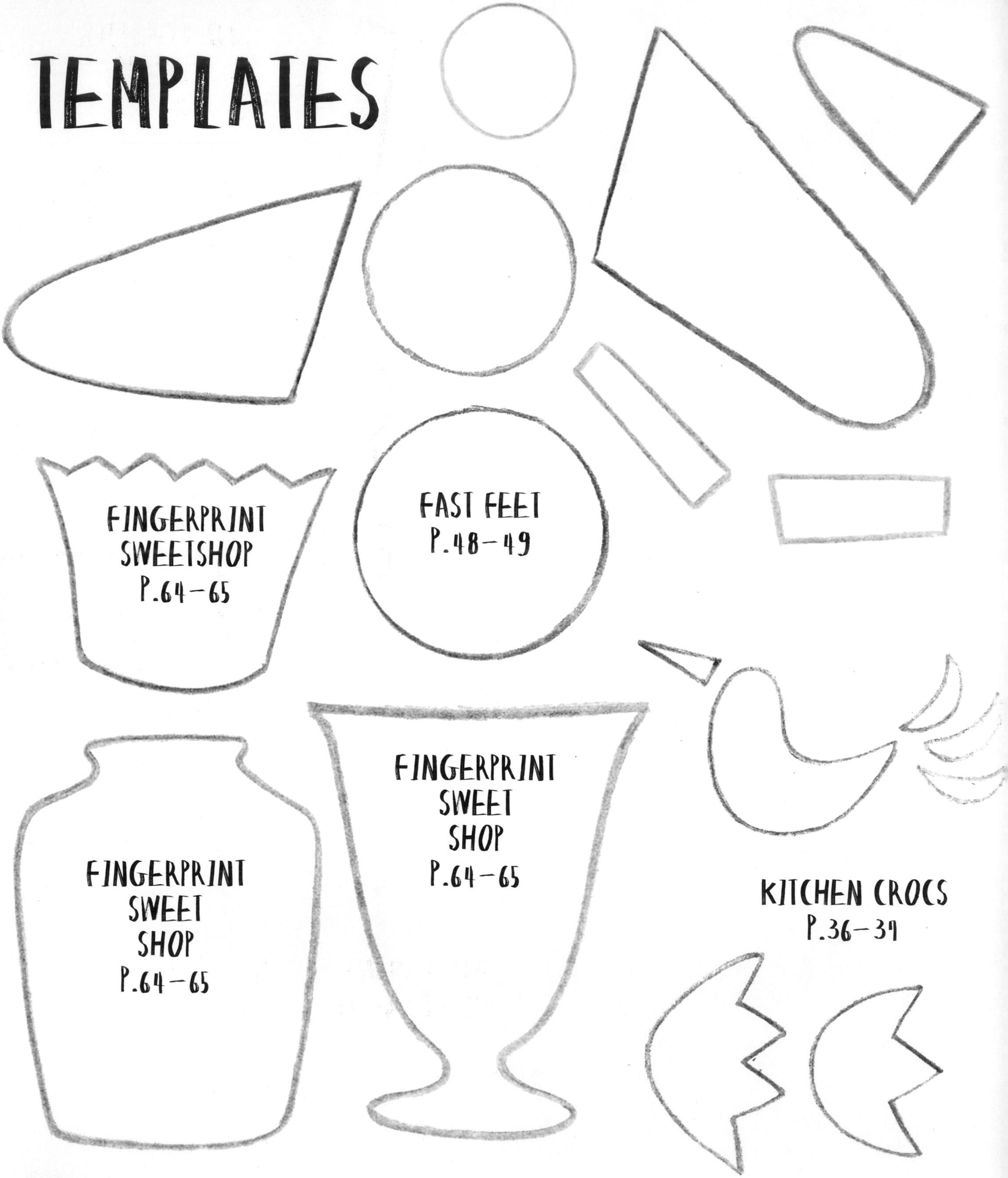

FINGERPRINT
SWEETSHOP
P.64—65

FAST FEET
P.48—49

FINGERPRINT
SWEET
SHOP
P.64—65

FINGERPRINT
SWEET
SHOP
P.64—65

KITCHEN CROCS
P.36—39

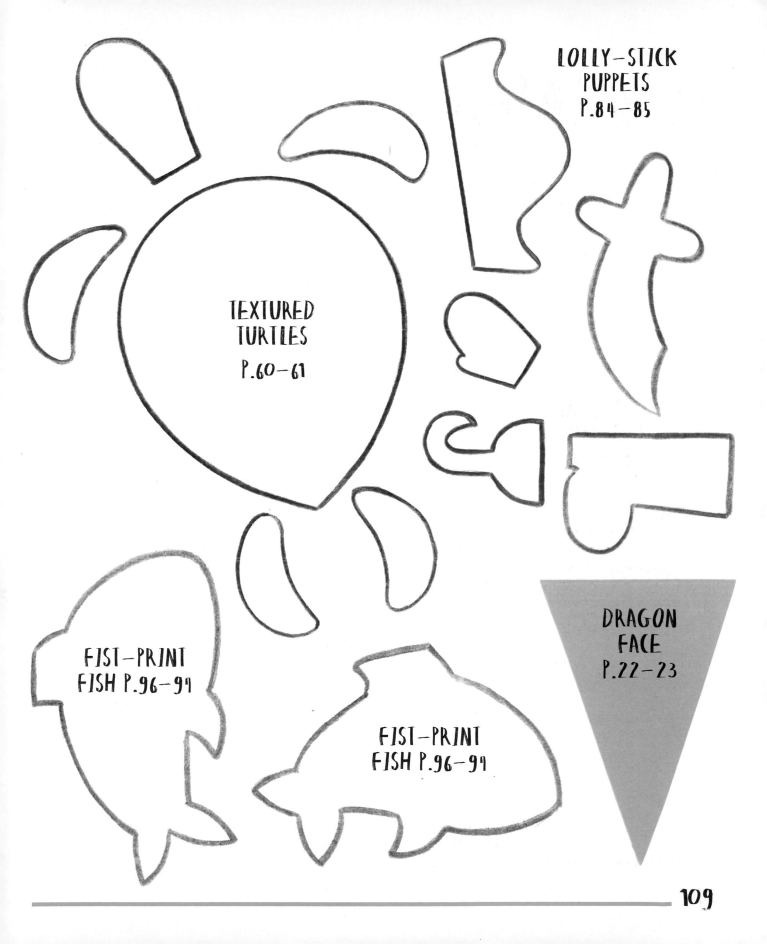

LOLLY-STICK
PUPPETS
P.84—85

TEXTURED
TURTLES
P.60—61

DRAGON
FACE
P.22—23

FIST-PRINT
FISH P.96—99

FIST-PRINT
FISH P.96—99

TEMPLATES

LEAFY LIONS
P.10–11

LEAFY LIONS
P.10–11

ICE–CREAM
BUNTING
P.28–29

SPOTS AND
STRIPES
P.50–51

ICE–CREAM
BUNTING
P.28–29

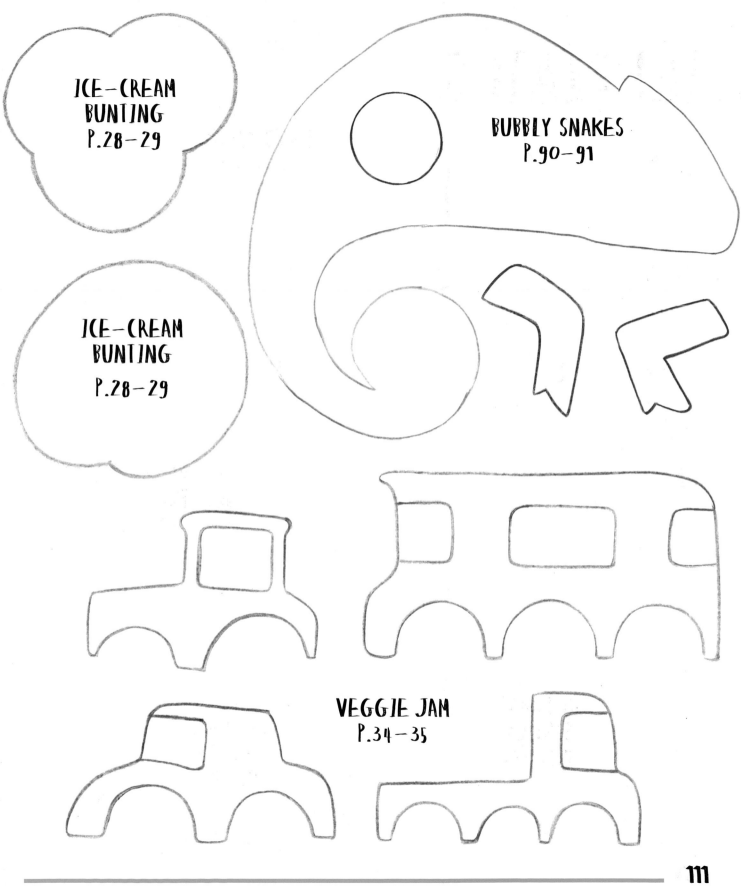

ICE-CREAM
BUNTING
P.28-29

BUBBLY SNAKES
P.90-91

ICE-CREAM
BUNTING
P.28-29

VEGGIE JAM
P.34-35

Published in Great Britain in 2018 by Wayland

ISBN: 978 1 5263 6020 5
10 9 8 7 6 5 4 3 2 1

Printed in China

MIX
Paper from
responsible sources
FSC® C104740
FSC
www.fsc.org

Wayland
An imprint of
Hachette Children's Group
Part of Hodder and Stoughton
Carmelite House
50 Victoria Embankment
London EC4Y 0DZ

An Hachette UK Company
www.hachette.co.uk
www.hachettechildrens.co.uk

Editor: Elizabeth Brent
Design: nicandlou
With special thanks to Bing Meddowes for the use of his hands and feet.